An Integrated Art Education

Smart 8

Level 1

This book belongs to :

Preface

Smart 8 is unique-for three reasons. First, it is designed to stimulate many sensory learning experiences, each carefully developed along its own track. Second, it introduces varied aspects of art, culture, social behavior, history, and science, each also carefully developed to progress cumulatively. Third, it does all this using language, graphics, and examples that appeal to children.

Each unit, at each of the four levels, provides a wide variety of inter-related activities. Children are challenged to respond to great art, to move, dance, sing, play simple instruments, count, answer questions, color, make comparisons, and investigate the real world around them. They learn about artists, composers, scientists, and historical events in a story-telling context, not in lists of facts or dates. The association with art, color, science, movement, history, and human behavior is direct and personal.

Art examples come from many periods, and each will appeal to a young child. Each artist writes a short letter that creates an attractive and simple way for a child to remember, and relate to, that artist. The music examples connected to each art work, and included on CDs that come with each book, also come from different periods and introduce different styles of music. The young child will hear orchestras of different sizes, keyboards, flutes, harps, and oboes. Each music example suggests and supports group and individual movement activities that encourage the child to use full body movements, not merely to tap or to clap. The sections in each unit that focus on the natural world-"science"-cleverly evolve from the art and music. History and artist "playgrounds" acquaint the child with different times and in different countries, and highlight the significant artists, thinkers, and inventors of these times and countries.

And-using these books is fun! There are games, stickers, things to color, places to draw, dots to connect, mazes to puzzle through, things to mix and match. These varied activities appeal to children with different learning styles and abilities. Some children love to create, some to fill in blanks, some to solve problems, some to act, some to ask questions. I think a program like this should be part of every school curriculum. Congratulations and thanks to the writer, designer, and publisher who have produced these books. A wonderful achievement!

Marienne Uszler

Editor and Co-Author of The Well-Tempered Keyboard Teacher
Former Designer and Director of Pedagogy Keyboard Studies at the University of Southern California School of Music

I strongly believe that learning is something we all want to do and yet so often we struggle with how to do it! There are so many options and too often options can seem like barriers. We can copy someone or something, we can bury our noses in texts, we may follow a diagram or a set of instructions, we can learn alone or with friends. Each path may be helpful for a while but one thing I have learned is that no one way is the answer! We all need to learn in different ways. This leads me to another important conclusion, namely that we all need to learn how to learn.

Children of today will have to solve challenges, the nature of which are, as yet, undefined. Fundamental to their successful solutions will be the strength of their creative thinking and problem solving, and the arts have a critical part to play in those. Smart 8 series is about learning how to learn through not only the arts but also a wider subject knowledge base. Key to its success is the belief that the development of successful creative thinking is to secure it as an on-going living process; a skill in itself that needs rehearsing, that crosses all subject areas and therefore embraces multiple areas of intelligence. The series Smart 8 has developed just such a range of integrated activities to give a context to and breathe life into creative thinking.

It is a complete joy to witness how children to learn to love open questions, and how they enjoy listening to each others ideas, sharing and valuing thinking - but always keen to make their own ideas heard! In Smart 8 children are guided through each activity in which they can happily engage with the excellent examples of specialist paintings, pieces of music, laws of physics and scientific matter. However they are also gently but constantly guided into addressing "why?" questions; "what do you think?" "what if?" In short, they are learning how to learn!

It is a great pleasure and privilege to have read this series and to have worked with children engaging in the activities. The books are so colourful and eye-catching for youngsters. I have seen how the pages have draw them into learning and engendered a desire to achieve. I too have found the pictures engaging, and been drawn into the wonders of the world that they have connected me with; why is there sand on the sea shore? How do I feel when the music is played and why is it important that these things connect in me? ….

Maureen Hanke

Head of the Norfolk Music Service
Lead Author of Music Express

An integrated art experience that will develop your children into global leaders!

Experiencing arts convergence activities will help your children develop into creative individuals who are academically well-adjusted, and capable of integrated thinking. They will develop appreciation for arts.

This book is written for future leaders in a rapidly-changing society.

The greatest paintings and classical music of all time have been selected in this series. Focus and physical development can be enhanced through dances like Minuet, Waltz, Ballet, poems and stories. Cultural experiences can also be enhanced through creative and imaginative conversations with interesting and fun characters in the book.
Each theme begins with logical ordering of trains of thought will connect the integrated activities in mathematics, science, and history. This aims to bridge knowledge gaps in various fields for the children to explore the vast world of knowledge and grow into happy leaders.

Happy Child

Artful Child

Global Child

Creative Child

Whole Learning through Artful Activities...

Smart 8 - An Integrated Art Experience

1. It targets the whole child and addresses different modalities of learning while integrating core content into art education.

• **Multiple Intelligence**

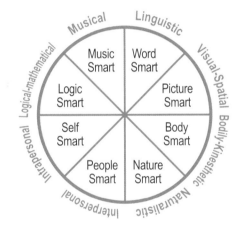

• **Whole Brain Development**

• **Healthy Habit of Body and Mind**

• **Motivation of Knowledge**

• **Communication Skill in School and Society**

• **Creative & Critical Thinking**

• **Appreciation of Artistic Wonder**

• **Comprehensive Musicianship**

2. It buds diverse seeds of knowledge.

3. The music CD in the book will be a valuable gift.

The CD will provide opportunities to interact and respond to art both visually and musically. With carefully selected music pieces, students are exposed to a variety of artistic expressions and given opportunities to develop their own artistic voice.

4. Share the experience as a family.

Sharing artistic experiences through music, art, poetry, and much more will provide a greater and stronger connection with your children. It will build character and provide a medium for bonding. It provides a guide for parents who are unsure of where to begin art education for children.

⚡ The icons for integrated art activities

 Poems & Storytelling

having curiosity and interest in paintings

 Think playground

strengthening critical thinking, linguistic intelligence, and social skills

 Music playground

developing musicianship through classical music and relevant activities

 Math playground

fun and creative math with animal characters

 Science playground

little scientists' lab

 Word playground

finding connections between words and elements from paintings

 History playground

experiencing different periods and culture through art

 Artist playground

benchmarking world's great masters!

 Global leader

growing leadership and confidence

 Let's create!

improving drawing skills and imagination

 Mission

problem-solving

 **Dr. ART**

understanding art techniques and acquiring wonderful taste

Contents

		BOOK	CD
★	**Children Playing on the Beach** - Mary Cassatt	08	① ⑦ ⑧
★	**Las Meninas** - Diego Velàzquez	18	② ⑨ ⑩
★	**The Apple Gatherers** - Frederick Morgan	28	③ ⑪ ⑫
★	**Ballet Rehearsal** - Edgar Degas	38	④ ⑬ ⑭
★	**The Starry Night** - Vincent van Gogh	48	⑤ ⑮
★	**The Gleaners** - Jean-François Millet	58	⑥ ⑯ ⑰

CD List

Music	Title	Composer	Musician	Story	Letter
1	**Rosita**	Tarrega	Mats Bergstrom	7	8
2	**Overture No. 2, BWV 1067 - VI. Minuet**	J.S. Bach	Cologne Chamber Orchestra, Conductor: Helmut Muller-Bruhl	9	10
3	**Entertainer**	Joplin	Nuyi Kong	11	12
4	**Sylvia - Pizzicato**	Delibes	Nuyi Kong	13	14
5	**Arabesque No. 1**	Debussy	Subeen Choi	15	
6	**Peasant Cantata BWV 212**	J.S. Bach	Budapest Failoni Chamber Orchestra Conductor: Matyas Antal, Ingrid Kertesi, Jozsef Mukk	16	17

01

Children Playing on the Beach

• Mary Cassatt •

Sparkle, sparkle,
Sand on the beach.

Splash, splash,
Waves in the sea.

Build, build,
Sand castles on the beach.

Let's build sand castles.
Let's look for pretty seashells.
It's fun to play together.

Oil on canvas, 1884, National Gallery of Art, Washington, DC

⭐ Look at the painting on the left and talk.

💡 Find a boat!
Can you name the boat?

💡 How is the weather?
Is it cold? Is it hot?
Why do you think so?

💡 Where is their mom?
Is she watching them?

💡 What do you think they are talking about?

Let's make a sand castle!

⭐ Panda is playing with a ball. Let's play ball, too!

 **Music playground**    CD1 Tarrega 'Rosita'

"Play the guitar! Just like me!"

⭐ **It is a perfect song for the beach. Make motions.**

① make a sand castle

Let's build a sand castle
(4 beats)

Waves wash away the sand castles
(4 beats)

② play tag

Catch me!

Let's play tag
(8 beats)

③ swimming

Let's swim
(8 beats)

⭐ **Connect the motions to the song.**

①	②	③	①	②
4 times	4 times	4 times	2 times	2 times

⭐ **Teaching tips**   Feel free to add or make changes to the motions. You can play instruments or play with a beach ball while listening to the CD.

⭐ **Your body is the drum.**
Tap your shoulders, tap your knees...
Tap any body part to the music!

⭐ **Play the tambourine or drum your hands on the table.** Let's count!

"**One** - two - three - four"

"**One** - two - three - four"

⭐ **Play beach motions on the tambourine.** This builds your piano technique!

make a sand castle

shake and mimic the waves

play tag with fingers

swim and tap,
one hand at a time

⭐ **Teaching tips** These activities teach you the steady beat. The beach motions don't have to be in order.

Mary Cassatt  CD8

1844-1926 Early impressionist, female artist.

Hello!

I am from America. When I was six, I visited Europe.

I fell in love with music ♫ and art. I also learned

French, "Bonjour!" When I was eleven, I went to

Paris ▮▮. I saw Edgar Degas's paintings and I

wanted to become an artist. Degas taught me about

painting. We became friends for life!

I love Degas and my sister Lydia!

I love painting so much that I never got married.

Mary Cassatt

★ Teaching tips Use the letter from the artist for storytelling and start a conversation.

12

"This is Cassatt's family!"

dad   mom

sister, Lydia   me, Mary

★ How many people are there? _____

★ Draw a family member.

Help Ms. Cassatt Mission

⭐ Find the original painting.

⭐ Draw pretty glasses on Ms. Cassatt.

Ms. Cassatt had bad eyesight.
It became worse and worse. She could not see.
What should we do to keep our eyes healthy?

13

Why is sand on the beach?

Waves break the rocks.

Wind breaks the rocks.

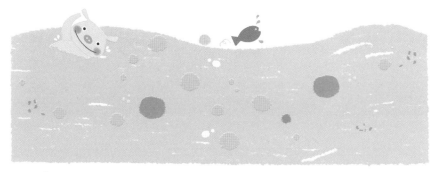

Waves bring the broken rocks to shore.

Big rocks sink and tiny sand remains.

There are beaches with no sand!

Strong waves wash the sand away. Steep beaches wash the sand away and only rocks remain.

Yay~ It's a pebble beach!

⭐ Color the picture. CD1

Let's play at the beach!

⭐ Place the stickers below. **Sticker**
Make conversation using the words.

sticker — sand

sticker — sea

sticker — boat

sticker — hat

 **Dr. ART**

Three Primary Colors

Red, **blue**, and **yellow** are **primary colors**. They are basic colors. You cannot mix colors to make primary colors.

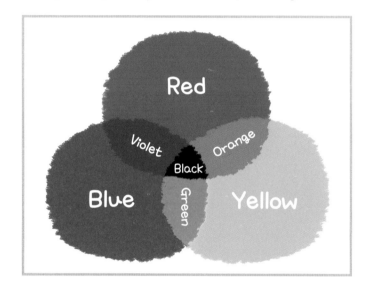

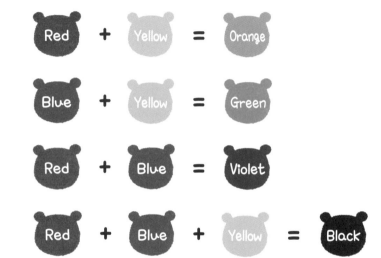

Red + Yellow = Orange

Blue + Yellow = Green

Red + Blue = Violet

Red + Blue + Yellow = Black

★ **Place the stickers below.** Sticker

Red

Yellow

Blue

"What color do they make?"

"Violet!"

★ **Teaching tips**   Try mixing colors using colored pencils or crayons.

Let's create!

Say the colors. Then color the picture.

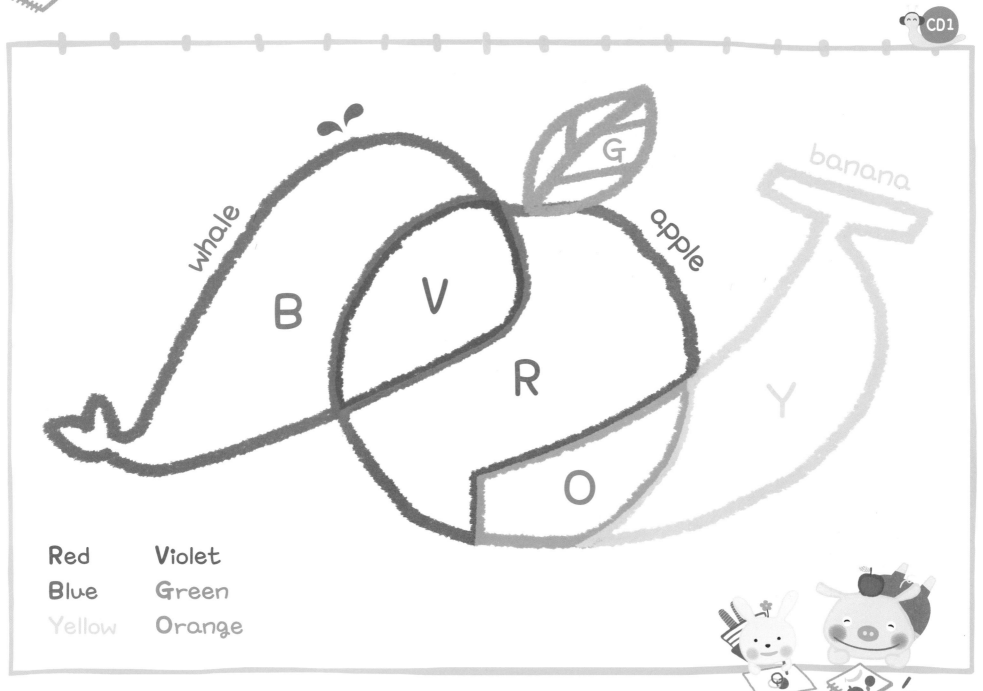

Red   Violet
Blue   Green
Yellow Orange

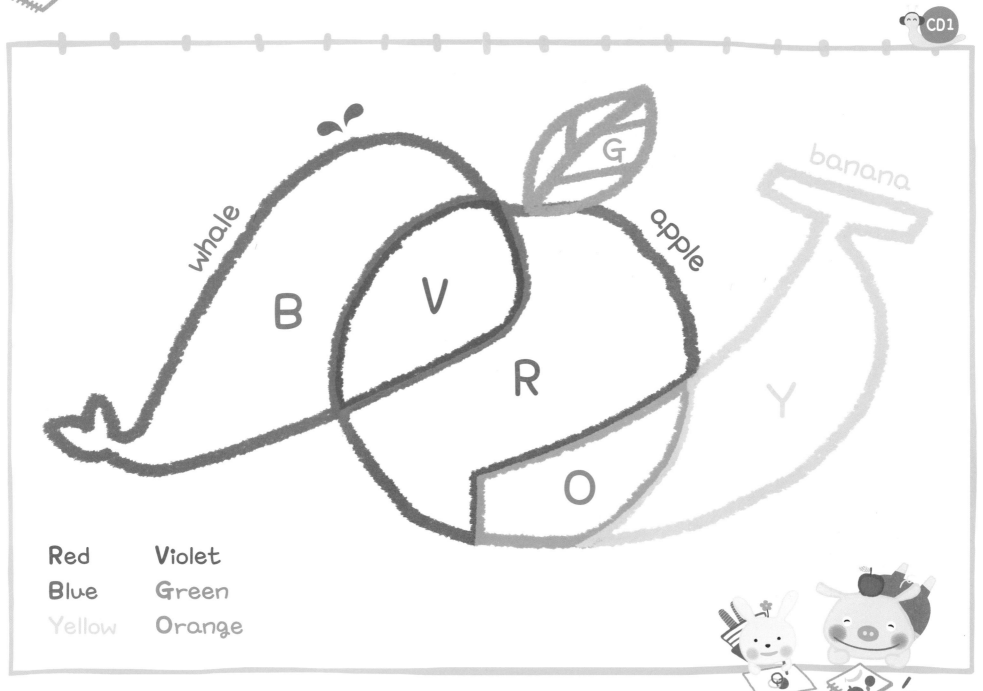

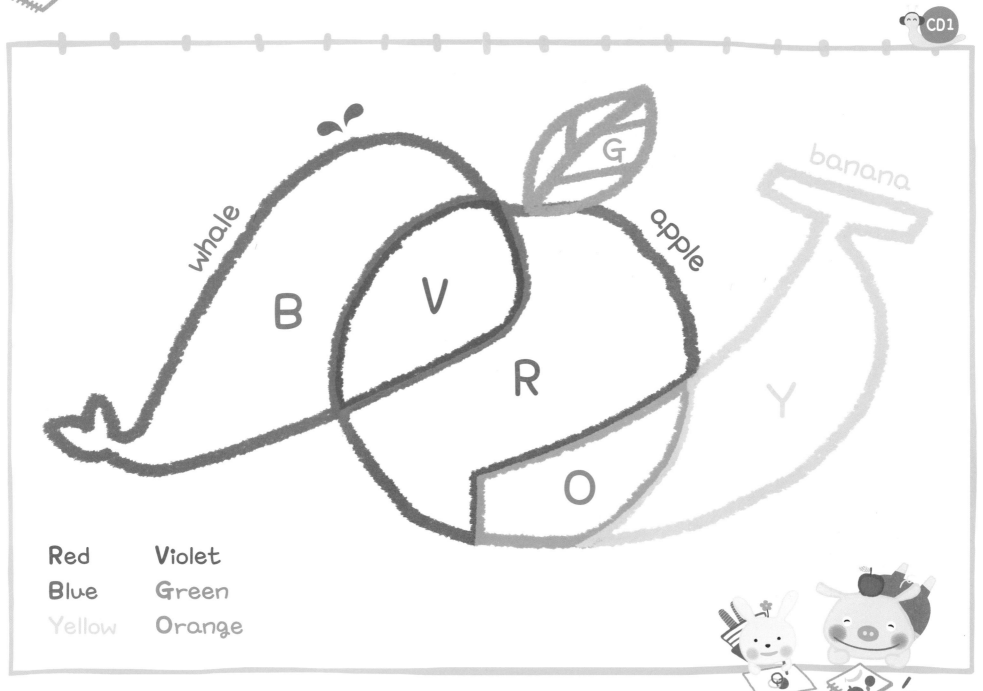

whale

apple

banana

B

V

R

O

G

Y

17

02

![Las Meninas painting by Diego Velázquez]

Oil on canvas, 1656, Museo del Prado

Las Meninas CD 2,9

• Diego Velàzquez •

Princess Margaret of Spain,
A princess from long ago.
You have a beautiful dress,
A dress from long ago.
Come and see me again
Let's say Hola! Hello!

Who do you see?
I see the artist. I see the maids.
I see the princess. She is 5 years old.
Do you see the king and queen?
Yes, in the mirror!
The artist looks bigger than the king.
Do you know why?

Storytelling

⭐ Look at the painting on the left and talk.

💡 Can you find the king and the queen?

💡 Can you find the artist? What is in his hands?

💡 What do you think the maids are saying?

💡 What do you think the princess likes? What kind of games would she play?

4 years old

8 years old

10 years old

"Princess Margaret died when she was only 21 years old!"

 Which maid do you want?

I read books to you.
I make yummy food for you.

I dress you.

I make you laugh.

 **CD2** Bach Overture No. 2 'Minuet'

Princess Margaret lived in the Baroque period. She listened and danced to the minuet.
A minuet is dance music with three beats ▲ in a bar.

⭐ **Count the numbers aloud and conduct.**

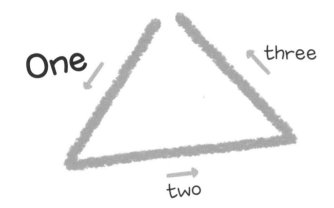

One
three
two

"**One** - two - three"

⭐ **Music has 'addition', too. 3 + 3 = _____   A minuet has six beats in a move.**

⭐ **Count to the music and clap your hands at ✦1✦ .**

✦1✦ - 2 - 3 - 4 - 5 - 6   ✦1✦ - 2 - 3 - 4 - 5 - 6

⭐ **Teaching tips**   You can use a scarf or play an instrument when you count.

Minuet comes from the word 'mini', which means small and light.
Move gently and dance elegantly.

"Listen to the Harpsichord."

⭐ **Dance to the Minuet.** Dance freely to the music.

① Step

ready. bow!

move **six steps** to the right

move **six steps** to the left

② Turn

turn **six steps** holding right hands

turn **six steps** holding left hands

repeat 1 and 2

bow in the beginning and at the end

⭐ Teaching tips   If students are too young to learn the minuet, let them dance freely to the music or make motions that fits 6 beats. (E.g., jumping rope, bicycling, going on a swing, shaking scarves)

Diego Velázquez CD 10

1599-1660 A Baroque artist who wanted to be a noble.

Hello!

I am Diego Velázquez the court painter for

Felip IV, the King of Spain. Not only do I paint,

I make the king's bed sheets,

I do the gardening, and I decorate the palace!

I also have to prepare for parties. I am so busy!

I want to be a noble.

Diego Velázquez

 My Day

☀ 6:00
I paint

☀ 12:00
I decorate the palace

☀ 17:00
I make the king's bed

🌙 20:00
I prepare for parties

 Tell me about your day.

⭐ Color the picture. CD 2

Hello, princess!

⭐ Place the stickers below. **Sticker**
Make conversation using the words.

sticker

sticker

The Baroque Period (1600 - 1750): A time in Europe with many fancy artistic styles

💜 Fancy clothes and furniture

Men wore wigs!

Louis XIV

Anna of Austria, Mother of Louis XIV

💜 Harpsichord, the grandmother of piano

two keyboards!

💜 J. S. Bach

Famous composer, organist

Bach's parents died when he was nine years old.
He studied music by himself!
He had 20 children.
He composed over 1,000 pieces of music.
There are over 50 musicians from the Bach family!

💜 Isaac Newton

Famous scientist, mathematician

Newton discovered the earth's gravitational pull when he saw an apple fall from a tree.

Place the ★ stickers on the correct answers. Mission

★ Find 2 animals dressed in the Baroque style.

★ What was Bach's job?

 chef    musician    policeman    fireman

★ What fell to the ground when Newton discovered the earth's gravitational pull?

 watermelon   chicken    apple    flower

★ Teaching tips   Try to express the sound of dropping a watermelon on the piano. How would you drop your hands to express the other items above?

25

Perspective

Find the servant standing on the stairs in 'Las Meninas (page 18)'.
Why is he so small? Is the servant shorter than the princess?

When things are **far**, we draw them small.
When things are **near**, we draw them **BIG**. We call this '**perspective**'.
In music, it is the same.
When sound is far, it is soft. When sound is near, it is LOUD!

★ Use 'perspective' and place Sticker the stickers on the right.

★ Teaching tips   Place your finger on the smallest car.
Follow the road with your finger and make the sound 'vroom'.
The sound gets bigger as the car gets closer.

A time machine brings the princess to the future.
Draw clothes and accessories for the princess.

CD2

⭐ **Teaching tips** You can copy the pictures or create your own clothes and accessories. You can also use stickers to decorate.

The Apple Gatherers • Frederick Morgan •

Oil on canvas, 1880, Private Collection

Climb, climb up the tree.
Shake, shake the apple tree.

One by one the apples fall.
Catch the apples with
the sheet.

One by one the apples roll.
Put the apples in the
basket.

Who wants one?
Who wants one?
I'll give it to··· you!

Hello, apple tree! I really like you! Your apples are so sweet and pretty.
I shake you. I tickle you. You are so kind to me. You give me all your apples.
You help me play hide and seek. Apple tree! I really, really like you.

03

⭐ Look at the painting on the left and talk.

The apple tree is tall. How would you pick the apples?

What can you make with apples?

What do you like to do for fun with your family?

What's your favorite fruit? Who would you share your fruit with?

⭐ Listen to the music and play catch the ball with a scarf(or a parachute). CD3

 CD3 Joplin 'Entertainer'

⭐ Dance to the music. (8 Beats for each motion)

climb~, climb~ up the tree

shake~, shake the apple tree

one by one the apples fall~

catch the apples with the sheet

one by one the apples roll~

put the apples in the basket

Who wants one? Who wants one?

I'll give it to··· You~

⭐ Point to the apples and count the beat. You can use an instrument!

🍎1 & 🍎2 & 🍎1 & 🍎2 &

Play for me ♪ Imagine the sound of an apple falling from a tree. Play the sound using a piano or other instruments.

⭐ Teaching tips 'Play for me' is a musical improvisation activity. Students can express themselves freely and be creative. Model using various dynamics and tones. Praise students on their unique expression.

30

Word playground

★ Color the picture.

I love fruit!

★ Place the stickers below. **Sticker**
Make conversation using the words.

Frederick Morgan CD 12

1847–1927 Painted happy children.

Hello!

I love drawing children , but

I'm not good at drawing animals .

So, my friends help me improve.

If you are not good at something, don't give up.

Ask your friends or your parents

for help. When you work together, you can do

almost anything!

Frederick Morgan

Help me draw···

Morgan

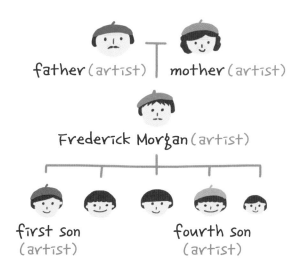

"Morgan's parents, wife, and sons were artists!"

father (artist) | mother (artist)

Frederick Morgan (artist)

first son (artist)   fourth son (artist)

★ Draw a puppy for Morgan.

Find the title for Morgan's paintings Mission

⭐ Match the paintings with their titles.

Sweethearts   See Saw   On the Beach

 Play for me

What's your favorite painting?
Look at the paintings and play the piano or other instruments
and express what you feel.

"I like
'Sweethearts'!"

How do **apples** grow?

⭐ Place the stickers below. **Sticker**

 sticker

You need water, sunlight, and soil!

Plant a tree.

sticker

Apple trees take 6 years to grow apples.

Grow the tree.

sticker

Flowers bloom.

sticker

Bees pollinate the flowers.

pistil

anther

The bee carries pollen from the anther to the pistil.

sticker

Yummy apples!

Fruit skin and Fruit flesh

⭐ Match the pictures by drawing a creative line connecting the same kind of fruit.

watermelon

strawberry

apple

orange

Real vs Fun

'Joong-seop Lee', a Korean artist painted 'The Apple Gatherers'.

Frederick Morgan

Joong-seop Lee

⭐ How many people do you see in each painting? _____ , _____

⭐ What is same? What is different?

⭐ Which one has more colors and looks real?

⭐ Which one uses a black pen?

"Which one do you like more?"

🎵 Play for me **Look at the paintings and play the piano in a style that reflects each painting.**

Let's create!

Pick your favorite apple and draw it. You can also draw your own apple!

How many will you draw? _____

CD3

Oil on canvas, 1873, The Fogg Art Museum

Ballet Rehearsal

• Edgar Degas • CD 4, 13

1, 2, 3, 4
Point your toes.
Look at
my pink toeshoes.

1, 2, 3, 4
Dance on tip toes.
Look like
a fluttering butterfly!

Mr. Degas, do the ballerinas pose for the painting all day long?
No, I remember the moment, imagine, and paint. I take a picture in my head.

 Storytelling

Degas

⭐ Look at the painting and mimic the ballet dancers.

Can you dance in front of people? How do you feel?

Ballet tells a story with dance and music.

What is the story of this ballet?

stage

toeshoes
It has cushions at the tip!

lights

choreographer
makes dance moves!

orchestra
Many musicians play different instruments together below the stage!

Edgar Degas, Orchestra

39

⭐ Point your toes and dance to the music.

⭐ **Show me how you feel.** Use your body to express different emotions.

 happy

 sad

 angry

⭐ Walk on your toes to staccatto.
Dance like a butterfly to legato.

⭐ Do finger ballet on the tambourine!

Use chopsticks instead of fingers.

⭐ **Teaching tips** Use your hearing and body to experience staccato, legato, and rest. Finger ballet makes your fingers and fingertips strong and trains finger independence.

★ **Follow the basic ballet positions.**
You can also make your own dance moves like a choreographer!

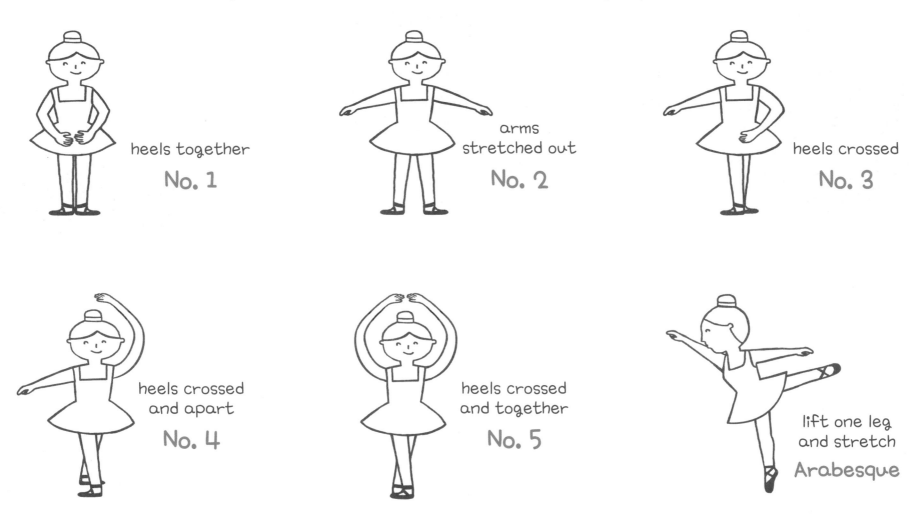

heels together

No. 1

arms
stretched out

No. 2

heels crossed

No. 3

heels crossed
and apart

No. 4

heels crossed
and together

No. 5

lift one leg
and stretch

Arabesque

★ Teaching tips   You can limit the ballet positions to just 1 or 2 or create other moves according to age groups. Show *The Nutcracker*, *Swan Lake*, *Sylvia*, etc.

Find Degas paintings  Mission

⭐ Match the paintings with the words.

practice room   orchestra   stage

"To the orchestra!"

"To the practice room!"

⭐ Color the picture.

CD4

I am a ballerina!

⭐ Place the stickers below. **Sticker**
Make conversation using the words.

sticker

sticker

Edgar **Degas** CD14

1834–1917 An artist who loved ballet and music.

Bonjour! ▮▮ France

I went to an art museum and fell in love with the

paintings. I copied paintings at the Louvre museum.

I visited art museums in Italy ▮▮ and practiced

painting. One day, I went to see a ballet.

Since then, I started painting ballerinas.

The brilliant lights! The orchestra ♫!

Can you hear the music in my paintings?

My best friend is a musician, Emmanuel Chabrier.

Edgar Degas

"He was friends with Mary Cassatt!"

Edgar Degas, Star

44

Global leader

What is your dream?

You need to believe, and try again and again. Your dreams will come true!

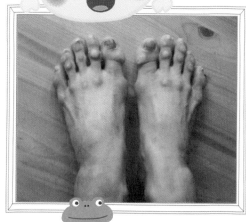

Whose feet?

They are Sue-jin Kang's feet.
She is a world famous ballerina.
She never stopped practicing.
She tried hard to be a better ballerina every day!

ribbit! Looks like my feet...

"Be patient, don't give up!
That's how I won
the Olympic gold medal!"

⭐ Who is your hero? What do you want to be good at?

⭐ To be better, what can you do?

45

You can make different dishes  with eggs . You can make different **ballerinas** , too.

Sculpture

Sculpture is a **three-dimensional** piece of art.
You can sculpt with **rock**, **wood**, **metal**, or even ice and soap!

Rodin, *The Thinker*

Degas, *Little Dancer of Fourteen Years*

Drawing

Draw with pencil before sculpting or painting.

Degas, drawings before Little Dancer of Fourteen Years

⭐ **Do you want to try modeling?** Give me your best pose!

Arrrggg!   Panda, the Thinker!

Let's create!

Let's draw **the** little dancer **with a pencil.**

Draw a line from 1 to 59. Side, front, back··· Which is it?

side

front

back

The Starry Night

• Vincent van Gogh •

Oil on canvas, 1889, The Museum of Modern Art, New York

Twinkle and swirl.
Stars come out
to play.

Twinkle and swirl.
Stars sing and play.

Shhh··· quiet,
The moon says.
It's time to sleep,
my love.

Looking at the stars always makes me dream! I paint the **night sky blue**,
violet, and **green**. I just love painting the bright stars one by one.
Do you know how many stars are in the sky? Let's count!

Storytelling

van Gogh

05

⭐ Look at the painting on the left and talk.

 Look at the painting.
Count to three and
close your eyes!
What do you remember?

 What do you
think the stars
and moon
talk about?

 Van Gogh paints
his hometown.
Can you tell me
about your town?

Let's make a wish!
What do
I wish for?

Make a wish
upon a star!

49

 **Music playground**

 CD5 Debussy 'Arabesque No. 1'

Debussy's music is as magical as van Gogh's brushstrokes!

Debussy

⭐ Use a scarf and do a swirl dance.

turn the scarf

throw and catch

dance with the scarf

fly the night sky

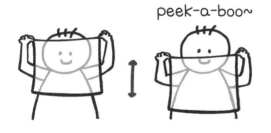

peek-a-boo~

stars peek through the clouds

clouds pass by the moon

⭐ **Teaching tips**   This music is effective for learning impressionism as it features rich, blended sounds from the use of the piano pedal.

⭐ Put a doll or an instrument in the scarf and gently rock.

rock-a-bye-baby~

play together!

⭐ Sounds can be high and low. Use your scarf to show.

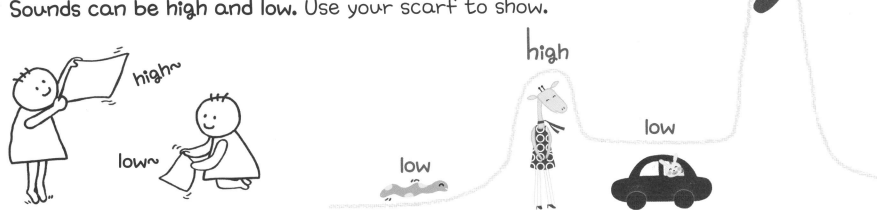

high~

low~

low

high

low

high

🎹 Look at van Gogh's painting and play the piano or instrument to express the tree, then a star, then the tree again! 🌳 - ⭐ - 🌳

⭐ Teaching tips Guide your students to understand the concept of music through play, like **high and low,** with the scarf.

Story of the Stars

The Little Bear

The Great Bear

Polaris

"Van Gogh paints the Great Bear!"

Hera, Zeus's jealous wife turns Callisto into a bear. Not knowing the bear is his mother, Callisto's son tries to shoot the bear. So, Zeus turns Callisto and her son into stars in the night sky.
They become the Great Bear and the Little Bear.

Oh, my son!

The Big Dipper

Can you see a ladle in the Great Bear?
That's the **Big Dipper**! Long ago, people used the Big Dipper to test their eyesight.

⭐ Connect the stars.

Seven stars!   Good eyes!

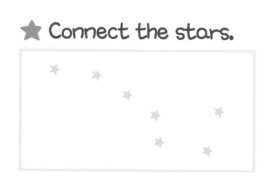

Word playground

★ Color the picture.

Look at the stars.

★ Place the stickers below. **Sticker**
Make conversation using the words.

- sticker — star
- sticker — moon
- sticker — tree
- sticker — mountain
- sticker — light

Vincent **van Gogh**

1853-1890 An impressionist who loved sunflowers.

"Van Gogh loved..."

♥ Bedroom

♥ Wagner's music

♥ Millet's art

♥ Sunflowers

♥ Yellow and blue

♥ Cypress trees

♥ Starry nights

 **This is me**

⭐ **Make your name card.**

name: Panda Kim

tel: (111)222-3333
home: 🏠 123 Red Road
(Nextdoor to 🐱)

Panda Kim ♥

⭐ **Draw things you like and share them with friends.**

things I like

⭐ **Teaching tips** This is an activity to develop introspective intelligence. Encourage students to introduce themselves with confidence.

55

Contrast

When things have differences, we call it 'contrast'.

An example of contrast in music is **big sounds** and little sounds.

\STOMP/

wriggle~

⭐ **Find the contrast.** Put a ⭐ sticker on the thing you like most. **Sticker**

Bright

vs

Dark

Sky full of energy

vs

Calm and Quiet village

⭐ **Teaching tips**   Use your voice or an instrument to explore; big−little, high−low, long−short sounds. Play a game making the opposite sound.

Let's create!

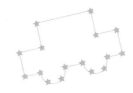

⭐ **Connect the stars.**
What constellation do you see?

⭐ **Make your own constellation.**

CD5

Play music that expresses your constellation.

Oil on canvas, 1857, Orsay Museum

The Gleaners

• Jean-François Millet •

Autumn is here.
Harvest is here.
Yo-ho.
The golden grains,
We gather.

Sunset is near.
Supper is near.
Yo-ho.
Home to the kids,
We go together.

We work hard to please our landlord. He says we can gather the grains
in the field. Today a new landlord will come. We'll dance and sing and welcome him!

Storytelling

⭐ Look at the painting on the left and talk.

 Mom works hard. How can I help?

 Do you see a horse? Who's on the horse? Why is he so small?

Can you find the colors of the French flag in the painting?

 Which season do you like most? Why?

Farming is so hard!
Thank you farmers for this food!

liberty equality brother-hood

The French flag

59

Music playground

CD6 Bach 'Peasant Cantata BWV 212'

In this music, peasants welcome the new landlord.

⭐ **The farmers have a party.** Let's dance and have fun!

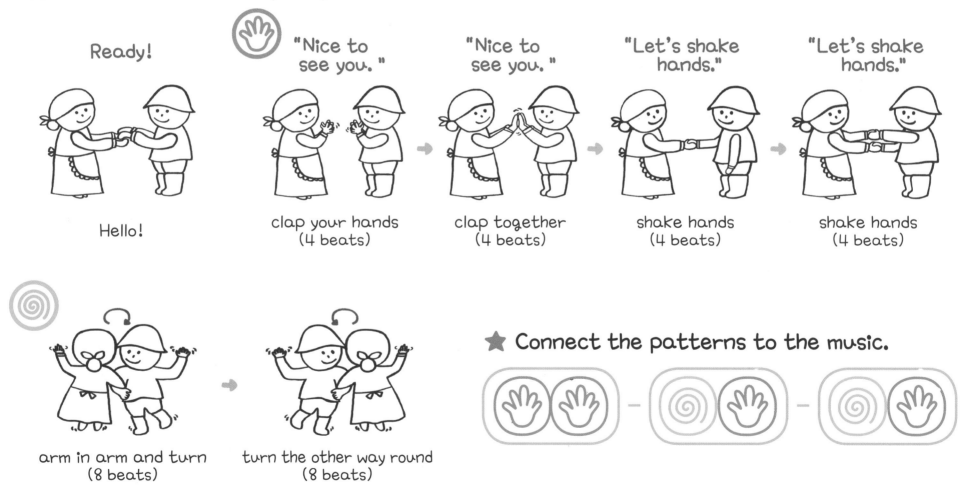

Ready!

Hello!

"Nice to see you."

clap your hands
(4 beats)

"Nice to see you."

clap together
(4 beats)

"Let's shake hands."

shake hands
(4 beats)

"Let's shake hands."

shake hands
(4 beats)

arm in arm and turn
(8 beats)

turn the other way round
(8 beats)

⭐ **Connect the patterns to the music.**

⭐ Teaching tips   Clap your hands and chant to the rhythm and dance. Create your own motion to replace "Let's shake hands".

⭐ Let's try farming to the music!

One-two

**plant
the seeds**

Stomp-stomp

**stomp
your feet**

Plow-plow

**plow
the field**

Pluck-pluck

**pluck
out the weeds**

Wipe-wipe

**wipe
your sweat**

Tralalala

**gather
the grains**

 **Express the motions using your instruments.**

⭐ **Teaching tips** Take time to talk about each farming action before you dance to the music.
The motions don't need to be in order. You can change motions according to the musical phrases.

Jean-François Millet CD17

1814-1875 Painted farmers's life.

Dear friends,

I don't like how artists only paint kings

and nobles.

I want to capture the beauty of nature and

the hard-working life of the farmers.

Artists like me, we live together

in 'Barbizon', a small village in France .

Come visit me and my friends someday!

Jean-François Millet

★ **Place the stickers below.** Sticker

Jean-François Millet

  France

· **Best Friends:** Barbizon School  Corot Rousseau

◇◇◇◇◇◇◇◇◇◇ Gallery ◇◇◇◇◇◇◇◇◇◇

The Angelus

Shepherdess with her flock

⭐ **Color the picture.** CD6

It is fall!

⭐ **Place the stickers below.** Sticker
Make conversation using the words.

⭐ **Teaching tips** Teach the seasons using words, sounds, and motions. (E.g., In spring, sprouts come up from the ground, 'boing'! Like a spring! In fall, the leaves fall to the ground, that's why it's called fall. Fall has another name, autumn.)

⭐ Tie 5 stalks of rice together into a bundle. How many bundles?

5 stalks of rice in

_____ bundles

⭐ Put 4 chestnuts on each plate. How many plates? **Sticker**

4 chestnuts each on

_____ plates

⭐ Put the same number of apples in the basket. How many baskets? **Sticker**

7 apples each in

_____ baskets

Find the differences

★ Find 5 things that are different from the original painting. CD6

"Found it!"

"Where?"

Picture playground

The Seasons

⭐ **'The Gleaners' feels like the fall.** Place the season stickers below.

Smith Walter Granville
'Two Ladies Ice Skating in Central Park'

James Tissot
'October'

Alma—Tadema
'The Years at the Spring'

Georges Seurat
'Final Study for Bathing at Asnieres'

sticker

sticker

sticker

sticker

 Play for me

Pick your favorite painting. Play the piano or other instruments in a style that reflects the painting.

⭐ Teaching tips   Talk about each season in detail and ask why they chose the particular season for each painting. An alternative activity is to listen to Vivaldi's *Four Seasons*.

Bingo Game Mission

⭐ Put the fruit and vegetable stickers in the spaces below. **Sticker**

Listen and circle the right answer. 3 in a row is a **BINGO**!

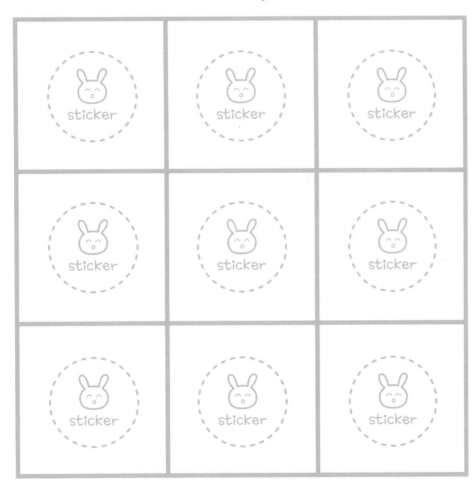

Quiz

- What's **red** with seeds on the skin? The seeds look like freckles.
- What's green and looks like curly hair or flowers?
- What's **brown** outside and white inside? French fries are made of this.
- What has many layers and makes you **cry** when you peel it?
- What has rows of seeds inside that look like golden teeth?
- What's a big, round, orange vegetable you see on Halloween?
- What grain is flour made of? We use this grain to make bread and cake.
- What **red** fruit is ketchup made of?
- What's an orange root vegetable that is good for your eyes? Horses like them.

⭐ **Teaching tips** The questions can be asked and read in any order. Give many clues. Tell them to shout "Bingo!" when they make a horizontal, diagonal, or vertical line.

Dr. ART

"Van Gogh practiced with Millet's paintings!"

Texture

Apples are smooth, pineapples are spiky. We call this **texture**.
How much paint you use, or **how** you use the **brush** changes the texture.
It's kind of like when we play the same song, but with the piano or the violin!

 smooth brush strokes

 wriggly brush strokes

⭐ **Look at the brush strokes and place the correct artist stickers below.** Sticker

sticker

 so smooth~

sticker

 wriggle wriggle~

68

What do you want to pick?
Draw what you want to gather.

 Flowers!

 CD6

Artist Achievement Award

Name: _____

This certifies that the student has

successfully completed **Smart 8** Level 1.

You may advance to Level 2!

Date: _____   Teacher: _____